Welcome

TO MY

CRAZY

LIFE

BLOOMSBURY EDUCATION
Bloomsbury Publishing Plc
50 Bedford Square, London, WC1B 3DP, UK

BLOOMSBURY, BLOOMSBURY EDUCATION and the Diana logo are trademarks of
Bloomsbury Publishing Plc

First published in 2020 by Bloomsbury Publishing Plc
Text copyright © Joshua Seigal, 2020
Illustrations copyright © Chris Piascik, 2020

A catalogue record for this book is available from the British Library

ISBN: PB: 978-1-4729-7272-9; ePDF: 978-1-4729-7270-5;
ePub: 978-1-4729-7271-2

2 4 6 8 10 9 7 5 3 1

Text design by Katie Everson

Printed and bound by CPI Group (UK) Ltd, Croydon, CR0 4YY

To find out more about our authors and books visit www.bloomsbury.com
and sign up for our newsletters

Welcome

TO MY

CRAZY

LIFE

Poems by

JOSHUA SEIGAL

ILLUSTRATED BY
CHRIS
PIASCIK

BLOOMSBURY EDUCATION
LONDON   OXFORD   NEW YORK   NEW DELHI   SYDNEY

Contents

Welcome!

Welcome to my crazy life:
I get up just gone noon,
and wander lonely over vales
while I hum a tune.

I gaze up high into the clouds
and contemplate the flowers,
then think of rhymes for 'daffodil' –
it often takes me hours.

I frequently bump into things
because my mind's elsewhere;
last week I tripped over the cat
and crashed into a chair!

Sometimes people seem to think
my job is not worthwhile;
they think I'm lazy, clumsy, useless,
strange and lacking style.

But my words shape humanity
although you may not know it.
The world *needs* weirdos just like me –
What am I?

I'm a poet!

2

The World's Worst Poet

There was a young poet called Josh
Who tried to be clever and posh
A limerick he wrote
But he hit a bum note
So he had to try something else.

A haiku is what
he then attempted to do.
But that was no good either.

Argh! He thought.
Can't I be good at anything?
Really, it can't be that hard.
Oh yes! I've got it -
Surely an acrostic isn't too difficult.
Today I will write an acrostic.
I can do that easily!
but it turned out that he Couldn't.

He then
turned his mind to
a type of poem called
a cinquain. *I've cracked it!* He thought.
But he hadn't.

Oh well, said Josh.
I'll write a novel instead...

How to Read a Book
For Every Child Our Future, Jersey

Conscientiously,
peering through a monocle
at each intricate letter

Cautiously,
tonging the toxic pages
between thumb and forefinger

Excitedly,
cracking the stubborn spine
like a chocolate biscuit

Angrily,
tasting bitter lava rise
at the back of your throat

Secretly,
under your desk
during a maths lesson

Vicariously,
over a stranger's shoulder
on the bus

Solemnly,
all alone
under the cloak of dusk

Lovingly,
huddled in the warm cocoon
of family

ZZZZZZZZZZZZAP!

Whenever something frightens me,
if ever I feel blue,
there's something very simple
that I'd really love to do;
the kind of superpower
that would conquer all my fears -
I'd simply point my finger and then

it disappears.

I'd zap away the bullies
and I'd zap away the ghouls,
and when the weekend's over
I would zap away my school.
I'd zap away my braces
and the pimple on my nose.
I'd simply click my finger and then

ZZZZZZZZZZZZZZAP!

 away it goes.

I'd zap away the angry words
between my mum and dad.
I'd zap away the arguments
that make me feel sad.
And sometimes, after having had
a truly dismal day,
I almost wish that I could even

ZZZZZZZZZZZZZAP!

myself away.

I'd zap away the demons
that reside within my head.
I'd close my eyes and hold my breath
and then I'd zap them dead.
I'd zap away the worries
that go on and on and on.
I'd take a gulp then give a wink and then I'd

ZZZZZZZZZZZZZAP!

them gone.

8

Whenever something comes along
and brings up all my rage,
and makes me feel like a tiger
trapped inside a cage,
I'd really love to zap it.
That's what I would like to do.
So do not make me angry or I might even

zzzzZZZZZZZZZAP!

    you

Anger

I snake my way through your ventricles,
spawning venomous vipers
in the chambers of your chest.

I am the tremors twitching beneath
your surface, your skin straining
to contain my poison.

I lurk like a limpet on ossified hearts
and seep like sap
from sharpened fangs.

I am a poet snapping a pen.
I am a monkey squatting on your shoulder.

I am anger.

I sneak through the cracks
in hardened concrete.

I cause rain to retreat to the sky
and clouds to get sucked in by the sun.

Babies know me before
they learn their first words.

My light says more
than all the letters in the dictionary.

I am the glue that fixes and binds.
I am the wind that carries life in its arms.

I am a monkey writing a poem.

I am laughter.

Silime!

as freezing as fire
as loud as a hush
as true as a liar
as dry as a gush

as hot as an ice cream
as sad as a joke
alert as a daydream
as small as an oak

as soft as a girder
as dark as white
as gentle as murder
as early as night

as wet as the desert
as huge as a pea
as bare as a sweatshirt
as normal as me!

The Coffee Monster

Marjorie is a mild-mannered woman.
She teaches at the local school.
Always smiling, always diligent,
she patiently helps the children
with their sums and spelling.

But, believe it or not,
Marjorie has a secret.
For every morning,
when the alarm clock beeps at the stroke of 6am,
Marjorie emerges from her cozy den
and becomes...

...THE
COFFEE
MONSTER!

Watch the hideous beast bare her fangs
as she prowls into the kitchen!

Gaze in wonder at her fearsome claws
as she rifles through the cupboards!

Marvel at her bleary eyes as she heaps majestic spoonfuls
into her 'World's Best Teacher' mug,

Gasp as she gulps down gallons
of her steaming potion.

Be amazed as she exhales deeply

and, just like that,
becomes Marjorie again –
a mild-mannered woman
who teaches at the local school.

My teacher said
to write a poem.
"Fill the whole
page up," he said.
Now I've done it
I think I will
go outside and
play instead.

Mrs Ironbladder

In Mrs Ironbladder's class
there's one exacting rule –
you're not allowed to leave
her lesson, ever.
You may find this ridiculous,
you may think that it's cruel
but it's no use playing games
or being clever.

If, for instance, you get bored
and say you need the loo
Mrs Ironbladder wields
her deadly power.
And even if you're desperate
and what you say is true,
you'll have to wait another
half an hour.

It doesn't make a difference
if you beg, cajole and plead,
she'll tell you viciously
that 'no means no'.
You can ask her very nicely
but you frankly won't succeed:
she simply will not ever
let you go.

So if you find that nature calls
in Ironbladder's class,
make no mistake, she won't
be very happy.
And since she'll never let you have
a simple toilet pass,
make sure you come prepared
and wear a nappy.

I Like Reading

I like reading Dad's old leaflets.
I like reading Mum's receipts.
I like reading things in secret.
I like reading in the street.

I like reading cornflakes packets.
I like reading magazines.
Lust for words? I do not lack it.
I read magic in my dreams.

Sad or funny, fact or fiction,
brochures, comics, I don't mind.
Atlases are my addiction.
Give me words and I'll unwind.

Menus, almanacks and journals;
sometimes even books from school.
Big fat chunks or little kernels –
reading is my rocket fuel.

You don't need to use 'howled' or 'growled'
or 'yowled' or 'cried' or 'muttered'.
You don't have to say 'wailed' or 'wept'
or 'yelled' or 'roared' or 'stuttered'.

You don't have to use 'moaned' or 'groaned'
or 'sobbed' or 'griped' or 'grumbled'.
You don't need to say 'giggled', 'sniggered',
'snorted', 'sighed' or 'mumbled'.

You don't need to 'expectorate',
'reveal', 'confess' or 'cachinnate'.
You don't need to 'affirm', 'allege',
'deliver' or 'pontificate'.

These words all have their uses
but maintain a level head:
sometimes, when you're writing,
it's OK to just say 'said'.

Summer

It's summer.
I want to be under my covers
catching up on cartoons.
I want to be up in my room
reading comics and re-ordering
my rock collection.
I want to be kicking a ball
against the garage wall.

Don't make me go
to summer camp.
Arguing, gossiping, being left out –
I had the whole of term time
for that.

It's summer.
I want to choose fruit with you
in the shops.
I want to come with you
to walk the dog.
I want to help you out
with the baby.

I don't want to go kayaking
or rock climbing
or football training.
I don't want to follow rules.
I don't want to keep sighing
and watching the clock
like I do every day
at school.

It's summer.

Don't make me go
to summer camp.

To a Special Person

You are my coat,
protecting me from the rain

You are my gloves,
warming my hands

You are my shoes,
anchoring my feet on the pavement

You are my glasses,
stopping me walking into dustbins

You are my jumper,
lying close to my heart

You are my belt,
keeping my trousers up.

The Both of Us

I used to be a butterfly
but now I'm just a slug.
I used to be a toothy grin
but now I'm just a shrug.
I used to be a rainforest
but now I'm just a tree.
It used to be the both of us
but now it's only me.

I used to be an estuary
but now I'm just a brook.
I used to be a library
but now I'm just a book.
I used to be a sanctuary
but now I'm just a zoo.
It used to be the both of us
but now there isn't you.

I used to be a dinosaur
but now I'm just a mouse.
I used to be a cityscape
but now I'm just a house.
I used to be a bakery
but now I'm just a bun.
It used to be the both of us
but now there's only one.

I used to be a symphony
but now I'm just a note.
I used to be democracy
but now I'm just a vote.
I used to be Mount Everest
but now I'm just a stone.
It used to be the both of us
but now I'm all alone.

Eye Like to Rhyme

I tried to write a poem
one fine evening, whilst at home.
I tried to do it properly
but the rhymes just wouldn't come.

Ideas swirled around my brain.
My head began to ache.
My heart beat ever faster
as I twirled on my moustache.

I really tried to concentrate.
I tried to think this through
but I started to get giddy.
I was feeling very rough.

"Oh what am I to do?" I whined
and asked my cousin Sean,
but he was less than helpful;
no ideas could he glean.

"What shall I do now?" I asked.
My stanzas numbered five.
My energy had been sapped out.
I gave all I could give.

Eventually I packed it in,
my mood was far too low.
I'd tried to make my poem rhyme
but I did not know how.

Stanley Stanza

Stanley Stanza owns some scissors.
They are special scissors –
with these scissors Stanley snips
poems into little bits.

There! See! He just did it!
He did it just then because
to Stanley Stanza, it seemed
the right thing to do.

Look! He did it again!
Sometimes he gets it right,
like he did just now.
Sometimes, however, he

seems to get it wrong.
Just like then.
And sometimes Stanley
Stanza
simply can't
be trus

ted.

What is a Poet?

A word juggling
world weaving
syllable smuggling
star breathing

stick shaking
show stopping
myth making
lip hopping

silk spinning
globe straddling
prize winning
brain addling

soul singing
sense saying
gold bringing
rent paying

fool.

What Am I?

I shine like a diamond.
I rain like cats and dogs.
I'm not doing this for my benefit.
I'm as soft as a feather,
as fierce as a lion,
as fast as a cheetah
and as small as a mouse.
I am more than meets the eye.
I'm always a bridesmaid,
never a bride.
I am like a kid in a candy store.
Avoid me like the plague.
What am I?

A cliché.

Alternative Haiku

Fly-ku

Buzz buzz buzz buzz buzz
Buzz buzz buzz buzz buzz buzz buzz
Buzz buzz buzz buzz buzz

Why-ku

?????
???????
?????

Buy-ku

£££££
£££££££
£££££

31

Pie-ku

Yum yum yum yum yum
Yum yum yum yum yum yum yum
Yum yum yum yum yum

π-ku

3.141
5926535
8979

Truly Frightful

There's an apple, some raisins,
a tangy satsuma,
some carrots and cranberries
fresh from the pack;
there's a pear and some walnuts,
bananas and grapes
in the scariest Halloween
trick-or-treat sack.

There's a juicy, ripe orange,
some broccoli florets
and lots of fresh greens
from the vegetable patch;
there's a plum and some peaches
and pineapple rings
in the scariest Halloween
trick-or-treat catch.

There's protein and vitamins,
minerals and fibre;
it's healthy and wholesome
and not nice at all.
It's a bag full of nasty
unspeakable horrors –
the worst ever Halloween
trick-or-treat haul!

It's useful for ghosts
(albeit uncool)
whenever it's raining
to wear a ka-ghoul.

The Nasty Box
After Kit Wright

I will put in the box

the bark of a dog, keeping me awake at night,
the graze on my knee from when I fell over,
lava from the mouth of a vicious volcano.

I will put in the box

a snowball filled with bits of dirt,
a fizzy drink that's gone warm and flat,
a stomach ache and a trip to the doctor.

I will put into the box

the deafening taunts of a thousand bullies,
a snarling teacher with furious eyes
and the red crosses on my failed homework.

I will put into the box

the time my brother told on me,
a burglar stealing a wedding ring
and a footballer with a broken leg.

My box is fashioned from decaying bark
with fungus on the lid and disappointment in the
    corners.
Its hinges are the knuckles of terrible ogres.

I shall bury my box
deep in the bowels of a dense forest
where, like a lost tribe,
it will never be discovered.

[Censored]*

The ▇▇▇ in this ▇▇▇ are not very ▇▇▇
Like ▇▇▇ and ▇▇▇ and ▇▇▇ and ▇▇

If you ▇▇▇ it you just might be ▇▇▇ or ▇▇▇
And then you will ▇▇▇ because of the ▇▇▇

Beware of the ▇▇▇ or ▇▇▇ ▇▇▇
It's not ▇▇▇ houses ▇▇▇ big ▇▇▇

▇▇▇ goats ▇▇▇ licks ▇▇▇ ▇▇▇ ▇▇▇
Eleven ▇▇▇ never ▇▇▇ stretch

▇▇▇ bat ▇▇▇ complain ▇▇▇ soup
Weirdly, ▇▇▇ never ▇▇▇ ▇▇▇ ▇▇▇

So if you ▇▇▇ and then ▇▇▇ ▇▇▇
Remember to ▇▇▇ so that ▇▇▇ aubergine.

*some of the words in this poem have been
blanked out by MI5 for security reasons. Can you
fill them in?

Where's Johnny?

Just where is he hiding?
He can't have gone far.
How can I find him?
I think it's bizarre.
In fact, it's an immense disgrace –
Why can't I find his hiding place?

Space Junk

They say
that bits of rusty satellite
float around
the sky at night,

that up there, just beyond
the earth's atmosphere,
hunks of broken debris
drift forlornly.

So I look up and think:
what else
might be stuck there
longing for warmth and love?

An alien's
homesick teddy, perhaps,
or an astronaut cut loose
from her spaceship.

Maybe there's a block
of cosmic moon-cheese,
or the spent match
that lit the Big Bang.

If I squint hard enough
I think I can make out
Saturn's missing
wedding ring

and a lost
love letter
from Neptune
to Pluto

just beyond
the earth's atmosphere
up there

        drifting.

Sticky Tape

Send out a search party!
Summon a crew!
I have a predicament -
what shall I do?
It's driving me crazy.
I've gone round the bend.
I need sticky tape
and I can't find the end!

I've looked high and low
and I've looked all around.
I've swum through the ocean.
I've crawled on the ground.
I've called a detective
who donned a black cape
but could not find the end
of that devilish tape.

I've roared and cursed coarsely.
I'm hoarse with inveigling,
searching the edge of
that round, sticky bagel thing.
This is a duff one!
This MUST be a con!
The end of the sticky tape –
where has it gone?

My eyes have gone crossed
and my skin has gone green.
My muscles have bulged
through my shirt and my jeans.
I howl and I growl
and I yowl like an ape:
"YOU MAY AS WELL ASK ME
TO PEEL YOU A GRAPE!"

I can't find the end
of the sticky tape.

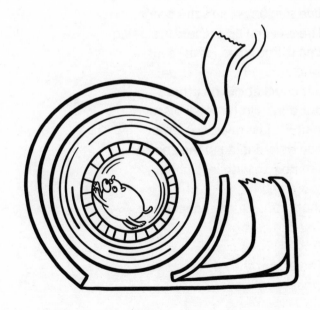

What's That Noise?

There is squawking, there is squalling
and a lot of caterwauling.
There is bellowing and bawling
and it's driving me insane.

There is shouting, there is squeaking
and a lot of rowdy shrieking
and it sounds like someone freaking
out in catastrophic pain.

There is screaming, there is crying
and it sounds like someone's dying.
There is growling, there is sighing
and it's gone on for an hour.

It's a racket like no other
but don't worry, you'll discover
that it's just my silly brother
and he's singing in the shower.

The Importance of Breakfast

Breakfast:
a glad tum.

No breakfast:
a tad glum.

Vegetaball

The Swedes were beet
at half-thyme.

The onions gourd
shallot of goals.

The cress headed a cross
from the parsnip's pass,

and the commentator
was a common 'tater.

Too Many Cats!

There are too many **CATS** in the house where I live
and I don't **CATS** know what to **CATS** do.
They're under sofas, on **CATS** the **CATS** shelves,
and even in **CATS** the loo.

CATS They're on the wardrobe and in **CATS** the sink;
they **CATS** lurk behind the door. **CATS**
They get where **CATS** they're not wanted –
far too **CATS** many to **CATS** ignore.

There are **CATS** on my mum and **CATS** on my dad,
above him **CATS** and below **CATS** him.
There are **CATS CATS** that get into every nook; **CATS**
there are **CATS** too **CATS** many **CATS** in this poem!

Not Enough   !

There are not enough   in the house where I live,
I wish that there were more.
I'd love a nice   when I get home from school,
barking at the door.

I'd take my   on nice long walks
through sun or rain or fog,
then I would give a juicy treat
to my little   .

I'd love to own a lovely   ;
I'd love to get to know him.
But there aren't any   in the house where I live
and there aren't any   in this poem.

Catastrophe

I am a cat.
I'm proud to be a cat.
Why is it, then, that humans
use me as an insult?

For example, when a human
stammers and stumbles
over their words, they say
I've 'got their tongue'.

And when a naughty little human
peeks over another little human's
shoulder, during a spelling test,
they get called a 'copy-cat'.

And what about this –
when a human shrieks
at the sight of a mouse,
they get called a 'scaredy-cat'.

Cats are not cowards!
Cats are fearless and loyal!
I wish these humans would stop
being so... *dogmatic*.

The Screaming Demon Cat from Hell

He's cute and sweet, with bright blue eyes,
but he's the devil in disguise.
He'll make you groan, he'll make you yell –

THE SCREAMING DEMON CAT FROM HELL.

Don't pick him up, you might get hurt.
You'll get his fur all down your shirt.
Who ate your fish? Well can't you tell –

THE SCREAMING DEMON CAT FROM HELL.

He'll mewl and hiss until he's fed,
confuse his toilet with your bed,
and just what is that noxious smell?

THE SCREAMING DEMON CAT FROM HELL.

He'll bring you gifts of mashed-up frogs,
he'll frighten off the local dogs
you'd better lock him in a cell –

THE SCREAMING DEMON CAT FROM HELL.

He's cute and sweet and small and white,
but he'll bring terror to your night.
He's Satan in a fluffy shell –

THE SCREAMING DEMON CAT FROM HELL.

Telling Porkies

I recently met
an invisible swine.
He looked quite unhappy.
He said with a whine:

"I'm not artificial.
This isn't a figment.
It's just that I'm missing
a small bit of pigment."

Can't Bear It!

I'm small and I'm grey.
I sleep in the day.
My body is covered with hair.
I hang out in trees,
and listen up please:
the one thing I'm not is a bear!

I'm not grizzly or polar.
I chew with my molars
because I eat leaves and not meat.
I'm not very scary,
I'm not at all bear-y,
I'm cute and I'm cuddly and sweet.

I'm friends with the roo
and the wallaby too
and the wombat is quite a good mate.
We all live in Oz
and we're happy because
our lives are relaxing and great.

So please don't be careless,
we're totally bear-less –
you won't find a bear around here.
And if you should DARE
to call me a bear,

well...

I won't do anything because I am cute
and small
and fluffy
and harmless
and adorable
and totally unlike a bear.

So there.

Level Scoffing

I'll zip along the rail
and I'll gobble up the track.
The ballast and the metal
make a tasty little snack.

I'll zoom across the mountains
gulping tunnels as I go.
I'll munch through rocks and boulders
and I'll slurp on dirt and snow.

Darting through the countryside
I'll dine on cows and sheep.
My engine's always ravenous.
I never, ever sleep.

The stationmaster signals
but I do not care a jot;
I'll hoover up the passengers
and guzzle down the lot.

Finally I'll eat the platforms.
Nothing will remain.
And that is why they say that
I'm a chew chew train.

Don't Forget Your Trousers

Don't forget your trousers
when you're walking down the street.
Make sure you have your trousers on
and shoes upon your feet.

Don't forget your trousers
when you catch the bus to school.
If you mislay your trousers
then you'll look a total fool.

Don't forget your trousers
when you're zooming down a slide.
Make sure you wear your trousers
on a roller coaster ride.

Don't forget your trousers
when you're visiting the zoo.
And don't forget to *pull them down*
whilst sitting on the loo...

Everyday Wizards

Every day, come rain or fog,
the wizards come to do their jobs;
come hail or sleet or cloud or sun,
the wizards' work has just begun.

The **TEACHER** shows you how to thrive;
she helps to keep your brain alive.
She puts up with the children's yells
(not all wizards use magic spells).

The **LIFEGUARD** bides his time until
you're drowning and you need his skill;
he'll rescue you from lakes and ponds
(not all wizards wave magic wands).

The **FIREFIGHTER** zooms straight round
with a nee-naw nee-naw sound
to save your soul from fire and smoke
(not all wizards wear a cloak).

The **SCIENTIST** discovers stuff
and studies things like flies and fluff;
she can discern the laws of motion
(not all wizards use magic potions).

If you have got a poorly pet
get on the phone and call the **VET** –
he'll mend your dog and cure your cat
(not all wizards have a pointy hat).

Yes every day, come rain or fog,
the wizards come to do their jobs;
come hail or sleet or cloud or sun,
the wizards' work has just begun.

Family Tree

In the autumn we take a trip
to visit my grandma's favourite tree.
"It's been there ever since I was
a little girl," she says.

Her tree is alone in the middle of a field
by the side of the road we always drive down
every time we come around
on our journey up from London.

Its once green leaves now crusty brown
with skeleton branches poking through,
its trunk stands firm and tall and proud
in the face of the changing seasons.

In the autumn we take a trip
to visit my grandma's favourite tree.
It is not dead, though it seems to be;
it knows that summer will come again.

Fairytale

Once upon a time
a boy called Jack
had a conversation.

He talked with some tuberous peas,
he gabbled with some garbanzos,
he conversed with some cannellinis
and he laughed along with some lentils.

He yapped with some yardlongs,
he mulled things over with some mungs,
he pontificated with some pintos
and he rapped with some runners.

And that, boys and girls,
is the story of Jack and the beans' talk.

Baa Baa Black Sheep Meets Thesaurus Rex

Pub, pub, atramentous conformist,
Acquire you each pelotage?
Affirmative monsieur, affirmative monsieur
Trichotomy haversacks abundant.
Solitary concerning yonder administrator
Solitary concerning yonder gal,
Plus solitary concerning yonder diminutive cadet
Which resides cascading yonder turnpike.

I'm **PRETTIER** than a princess

STRONGER than a gorilla

CLEVERER than a professor

CUTER than a kitten

FASTER than a torpedo

RICHER than a sultan

FUNNIER than a clown, and

SWEETER than an ice cream.

What am I?

A liar.

I'M

CAST AWAY

ADRIFT AT SEA

IT SEEMS THAT THEY'VE

FORGOTTEN ME. IT'S NOT A HAPPY

THING TO BE, A CHRISTMAS TREE

IN

JANUARY

Anxiety

There's a tightness in my stomach.
There's a tingle in my brain.
There's an adder in my bladder
and a viper in my veins.

There's a ringing in my ears.
There's a stiffness in my neck.
There's a lizard in my gizzard
that I cannot keep in check.

There's a storm in my aorta.
There's a bullet in my back.
There's a lion and it's trying
to embark on an attack.

There's a splinter in my sphincter.
There's a groaning in my bones.
Don't make me go outside today –
I want to stay at home.

Dealing with Fear

Make friends with her.
Open up your lunchbox
and give her a sandwich.
Take off her running shoes –
the ones with holes
and worn out soles –
and cast them away
to the bottom of your wardrobe.
Give her some slippers.
Write her an invitation.
Make her a cup of tea.
Put stabilizers on her bike.
Run a warm bath
and give her some armbands.
Wrap her up in a dressing gown
and sit her down on the sofa.
She has a story to tell?
Listen to the story.
Smile and nod politely.

Make a place on your fridge
as you would
for a three-year-old's
finger painting.
She's little.
She has a lot to learn.
Why don't you teach her?

You're Never Too Big for a Hug

You're never too big for a hug.
Some folk might seem smiley and smug,
but when the tears roll
and you're losing control,
you're never too big for a hug.

You're never too old for a squeeeeeeeeze,
for life offers few guarantees.
So when you're disjointed
and feel disappointed
you're never too old for a squeeze.

You're never too tough for a cuddle
if you are confused and befuddled.
When clouds gather in
and you feel in a spin,
you're never too tough for a cuddle.

You're never too cool for embraces.
You may think you know where your place is,
but if you're left out
do not be in doubt:
you're never too cool for embraces.

You're never too big for a hug.
It's nice to feel cozy and snug.
So turn to your neighbour
and do them a favour
and give them the gift of a **HUG**.

For the first time in ages all the family is together.
Everyone is together, and I've had my favourite meal.
They are fussing over me, tickling behind my ears
like they've done a thousand times before.
These ears that have pricked at a thousand doorbells
don't hear so well anymore.
These legs that have chased a thousand squirrels
have lost their zip.
This nose has sniffed a thousand bottoms
but now mostly snuffles against warm blankets.
These paws are losing their grip

but this heart still pumps with the love it has felt
for sixteen years, since they brought me home.
This head is misted with memories:
bounding through snow that first, excited winter;
lapping at the sprinkler when summer licked the
    lawn;
yapping on the stairs every morning at dawn
and leaping on the couch
when I knew that I shouldn't.

For the first time in ages all the family is together.
Everyone is together, and we're in this room.
I've been here once or twice before
but this time it seems different.
This morning the woman with the white gloves on
is not adorned with her usual smile.
This morning a heaviness hangs from the walls.
The faces around me are puffed with apologies
as clouds collect outside the window

but through the clouds I can see the sun
with a whistle in its mouth sounding notes for me.
I can see the trees waving silently
and the birds dancing with something like joy.
The sky is calling me:
"Good boy! Good boy!"
The sky is calling:
"Good boy..."

For the first time in ages all the family is together.
Everyone is together, and I'm getting tired.
I've just eaten my favourite meal
and they're fussing over me.
There's the woman in white, with the white gloves on
and my family are tickling behind my ears
and their faces are swimming out of focus
and I think I can smell the salt in their tears
and although these ears don't hear so well
I can hear the love of sixteen years
and I want to tell them I love them too.

I want to tell them I love them too
but I feel tired now; so tired   so tired
I feel tired now. So tired

Get Writing!

Hello everyone; it's Josh here! I am delighted that you have read the poems in this collection (or perhaps you just skipped to the end – naughty, naughty!). I hope that you enjoyed reading some of the fruits of my brain, and I very much hope you have even more fun writing some poems yourselves. Here are some ideas to help get you started.

My poem 'How to Read a Book' (p. 5) uses what posh people call 'fronted adverbials' – that means that each adverb comes at the beginning of the line or sentence. This can be an effective way of giving rhythm and depth to your poem. Start by thinking of an activity, such as playing football, acting in a play or doing a dance. Next, write down a list of *ways* in which you or someone else might do the activity. Using dancing as the activity, your list might look like this:

Elegantly
Flamboyantly
Angrily
Heavily

Finally, using each adverb as a fronted adverbial, complete the line. Here is an example to get you started:

How to Dance

Elegantly,
gracing the stage like a lithe swan...

To a Special Person

My poem 'To a Special Person' (p. 23) uses metaphors to describe a person who is special to me (I'm not going to tell you who the person is – it's a secret!). You can do something similar. Begin by writing down a list of objects that are special to you. These can be physical objects, like your bed or your glasses, or they could be more abstract, like the wind, the sun or happiness. Next, see if you can use your objects as metaphors to describe your special person. The trick is to try and think of something that the object and your person has in common. You might end up with a line like this:

You are my bed
providing my life with warmth and comfort...

Boxes

My poem 'The Nasty Box' (p. 36) is an homage to Kit Wright's poem 'The Magic Box'. You may have read that poem – it is very famous, and much copied. It is fun to create your own box, and fill it with all kinds of imaginative things. The key to this type of poem is firstly to give your box an interesting title, and secondly to describe its contents using poetic vocabulary. Here are some ideas for boxes that you might want to fill up:

The Scary Box
The Beautiful Box
The Sad Box
The Music Box
The Memory Box

Blackout Poems

My poem 'Censored' (p. 38) is pretty weird, and you as a reader have to do a lot of work to fill in the missing words. Luckily for you there are no right or wrong answers, and I have constructed the poem so that, whatever you write, the poem will be very, very weird! You can do something similar with your friends. Start by writing a poem, about anything you like and in any style. Then get rid of some of the words, so that the poem has gaps in it. Finally, get your friends to fill in the gaps using their own ideas. I promise, you will end up with some extremely weird and wonderful poems!

Thesaurus Poems

I bet you thought '*Baa Baa Black Sheep* meets *Thesaurus Rex*' (p. 64) was a very strange poem, and you'd be right; it is the weirdest poem I have ever written! The poem uses lots of words that I had never seen before. I got the words out of a thesaurus, which is a book that lists words that mean the same thing together. I started off by taking the nursery rhyme *Baa Baa Black Sheep* and then, using a thesaurus, I exchanged each of its words for a synonym. You can do this very easily; simply take a nursery rhyme and change the words using a thesaurus. Read them out to your friends and see if they can guess which nursery rhyme your poem is based on. Hours of fun!

Alphabetical List of Poems

Acknowledgments

'The Both of Us' first published in *Poetry For Change: A National Poetry Day Anthology*, Otter-Barry Books (2018); 'What Am I?' and 'Better' first published in *I Am a Jigsaw*, Roger Stevens (ed.), Bloomsbury (2018); 'The Nasty Box' first published in *Is This a Poem?*, Roger Stevens (ed.), Bloomsbury (2016); 'Space Junk' first published in *Spaced Out*, Brian Moses and James Carter (eds.), Bloomsbury (2019). All poems © Joshua Seigal.